Mia's Forest Rescue

1 **B**uild the LEGO® Miniset to create a tree-branch home for Goldie.

2 **R**ead the story about the friends' adventure in the Whispering Woods.

3 **C**omplete the activities and spend some time with Andrea, Olivia, Emma, Mia, and Stephanie!

Goldie

Pet Personalities

The friends have found a website that tells them which animal resembles each of their personalities the most! Read the descriptions about each girl and decide which pet you think is her best match.

Olivia

Animals

Frog

Bird

Hedgehog

Cat

Andrea loves singing and can't imagine her life without music. When she's performing, she feels like there's nothing that can bring her down. Andrea also loves hanging out with her friends and enjoys sunflower seeds. They're her favorite snack!

Andrea

Bird

Emma

Sign In →

Which Animal Would You Be?

Olivia loves coming up with new science experiments. It takes a lot of quiet and concentration to design her inventions, so she can come across as a bit of a "loner." But she always appreciates spending time with her friends. At nighttime, Olivia's favorite drink is a tall glass of milk.

I Cat

Mia

Mia is strong and sporty but also very graceful. She loves freedom, independence, and spending time in the great outdoors. For a snack, she enjoys eating crunchy carrots. And one of Mia's favorite things about herself is her long, red ponytail.

Horse

Butterfly

Dog

Bunny

Horse

Emma has a bubbly and creative personality. She adores fashion and draws her inspiration from nature's colors. Emma chooses clothes with fun textures, flowery patterns, and rainbow hues. Her friends know she can be a bit flighty sometimes, but they appreciate her beautiful sense of style.

Butterfly

Stephanie

Stephanie enjoys having a good time and making others laugh. Everyone in Heartlake City knows that she's one of the most loyal, reliable girls in town. Stephanie is always willing to keep a friend company, whether it's walking through the park or running along the beach.

Dog

Dream Lanterns

The friends are releasing paper lanterns into the sky. They've each written a special dream on one lantern. Can you match the lanterns to the correct girls?

Do you share any of the friends' dreams, or are yours completely different? Write your dreams on the empty lanterns.

Stephanie
Throw a spectacular party to celebrate the first issue of my magazine.

Emma
Design the most beautiful gowns for top celebrities.

Make the most beautiful flower that glows.

Olivia

Capture a photo of a rare butterfly no one has ever seen.

Mid

Create a place where all animals feel safe and happy.

Use your heart to make the most beautiful flower in the whole wide world.

Andrea

Record an album and have every song become a hit.

With your best friend, write down your secret dreams on pieces of paper together. Put the papers in a box and, with a parent's help, bury it in the yard. Who knows? Maybe your dreams will come true one day!

Mia's Forest Rescue

It was a crisp fall day in Heartlake City. Mia had just finished her classes at school, and she was hurrying to the Heartlake City Vet. Every Thursday, she helped Olivia's aunt, Sophie, take care of the animals. Mia couldn't wait to see what she needed help with today!

When Mia arrived, she found Aunt Sophie on the phone. "Uh-huh . . . uh-huh," Aunt Sophie was saying. She scribbled an address on a piece of paper. "All right, I'll be right there."

"What's up?" Mia asked as Olivia's aunt placed down the receiver.

"It's a good thing you're here," Aunt Sophie replied. "That was Mrs. Jones. Her dog has been eating pine cones again. She needs me to come over."

"Is there anything I can do?" Mia asked.

"Would you be able to wait here while I go to help her?" Aunt Sophie asked, swinging a coat over her shoulders. "We're expecting a delivery of special birdseed. It should arrive any minute."

"You can count on me!" Mia gave a little salute. Then she looked out the window. "In fact, it looks like you can count on all of us!"

Just as Aunt Sophie ran out the door, Emma, Olivia, Stephanie, and Andrea came up. Olivia was carrying Goldie the bird on her shoulder. Andrea pulled along a cart with a little puppy named Scarlett inside. And Stephanie trailed behind, riding on her quad.

"Hey, guys!" Mia called. "How's it going?"

"Not so great." Olivia shook her head. "I have a problem. Actually, *Goldie* has a problem. I can't get her to stop eating the seeds from my parents' garden. My mom is going to flip when she sees the seeds are gone *again*."

Andrea giggled. "For such a little bird, she sure has a big appetite!"

"Even this didn't help," Emma said, holding up a funny-looking puppet on a stick. It was made out of a tin can with a face drawn in marker. Shiny bits of foil and tinkling bells were glued to the sides.

"It's a scarecrow," Emma explained. "It was supposed to scare Goldie away from the garden."

"Except the only one it bothered was my dad," Olivia said. "The bells jingle with the slightest breeze. So he hasn't been able to sleep for a week."

"That's too bad," Mia said. "I'll ask Aunt Sophie if she has any ideas when she gets back."

Just then, the phone rang again. Mia ran to answer it. A minute later, she returned to her friends with a worried look on her face.

"That was the driver of the seed-delivery truck," she said. "He's supposed to be bringing a special order of birdseed this afternoon. But he's lost somewhere in the Whispering Woods. And his cell-phone battery is dying. The line cut out before he could tell me where he was."

"Poor guy," said Andrea. "It will be dark in a few hours. If only we could help him."

"We can!" Stephanie exclaimed, hopping back on her quad. "Come on, girls. It's time to go on a rescue mission!"

Story continues on page 14

Musical Inspiration

The popular band GREEN-TEAM is sweeping the city with its innovative form of music. Our top reporter scored an interview with the band's leader.

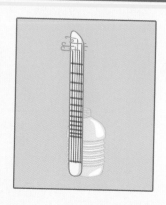

— **Your band composes some of the most unique songs I've ever heard. Can you tell me what makes you so original?**

I think it's not the type of music we play but the instruments we use. They aren't ready-made. We make them out of recycled materials.

— **Like changing an old guitar into a new one?**

Not exactly. We look for things which aren't useful anymore and give them a second life. For example, we have a guitar made of an empty plastic bottle, a plank, and bicycle spokes. We also have drums made of old pots, bowls, and plastic barrels.

— **That's amazing. What else can you make?**

Pretty much anything. The sky's the limit. But you'll need to wait until our upcoming concert to see our latest instruments. In fact, we have a surprise for your readers. Whichever fan mails us the most interesting idea for a new recycled instrument will get a free ticket to our next concert!

Do you want to know what the most popular accessory at the Heartlake City Pet Salon is? Color the grid according to the numbers to find out! Each number shows how many squares should be colored in pink, green, and blue per row.

Find the hidden picture in the grid to see which accessory is keeping Heartlake City's pets pretty!

16																
16																
3 1 8 1 3																
2 3 6 3 2																
1 5 4 5 1																
1 6 2 6 1																
1 6 2 6 1																
1 6 2 6 1																
1 6 2 6 1																
1 5 4 5 1																
2 3 6 3 2																
3 1 8 1 3																
16																
16																

Joke Corner

One day, Sara called for her mother. "Mom, look! I can write!"

"What did you write, honey?" her mom asked.

"I don't know. I can't read yet," Sara answered.

Silly Story

There's always something exciting happening at the Heartlake Pet Salon! Number the pictures in the correct order to read the funny story about Suzie, Stephanie, and Jessica at the salon.

For even more fun, fill in the empty speech bubbles with your own silly dialog!

Hi, Suzie! What's going on?

Hi, Jessica! I'm going to play Little Bo Peep in a new movie! But I need Fluffy to look like my lost sheep.

Now, just a few finishing touches and she'll be ready.

You did it, Jessica! Fluffy is the most stylish sheep I've ever seen!

Lets go fluffy. And by the way, to bye!

4

Oh my gosh! She's so cute!

2

Friends :)   Mommy   Daddy

Mia: Hi, Steph! I saw the pictures of Fluffy. The new style you and Jessica gave her is un-BAAA-lievable!

Stephanie: It's all in a day's work. ;-)

Quickly, the girls ran over to Olivia's Invention Workshop and grabbed a set of walkie-talkies. "These will come in handy in case we need to split up in the forest," Olivia said.

Then Stephanie drove them on her quad to the Whispering Woods.

"I'm going to head to the flight school to get the sea plane," Stephanie said. "It will be easier if we search for the driver on the ground *and* from the air."

"Sounds good." Mia nodded. "See you later!"

As Stephanie drove away, the girls tested the walkie-talkies.

"Come in, Andrea. Do you read me, over?" Olivia said into hers.

"I read you loud and clear," Andrea replied. "Are you sure it was a good idea to bring Goldie? The forest is so big, and Goldie is so little, over."

"It's okay," Olivia said. "Goldie knows to stay with me. Let's head toward the forest road that leads to the next town. Maybe the driver's there, over."

The girls walked into the woods. Sunlight filtered through the leaves, casting shadows on the ground. Every so often, a bird would chirp from up above in the tree branches.

WHISPERING WOODS

HEARTLAKE CITY

"*Tweet!*" Goldie would reply.

"Goldie, you're so musical!" Andrea smiled.

Suddenly, the little bird flew off of Olivia's shoulder.

"Goldie, come back!" Olivia cried.

The girls chased the bird along a winding path. At a fork in the road, Goldie zipped down to the ground. She began pecking at a pile of seeds.

"Leave it to Goldie to find the only spot in the forest with seeds instead of nuts." Olivia laughed.

"Olivia, you're right!" Mia gasped. "These seeds don't belong here. They must be the driver's. Maybe one of his bags ripped and the seeds are falling out. Let's see where they go."

The friends followed the trail of seeds. Goldie munched as they went. After a little while, Goldie suddenly stopped. She flew back to Olivia's shoulder.

"I think that means she's had her fill." Andrea giggled.

"Then it's our turn." Olivia shrugged.

"You want us to *eat* the seeds?" Emma asked, doubtful. "I mean, they are healthy, but . . ."

"No, silly," Olivia said. "We'll just lead the way instead of Goldie."

The girls continued deeper into the woods. Soon, they heard a car engine.

"It's coming from over there," Mia exclaimed.

A moment later, the path opened up into a clearing in the forest. Sure enough, there was the lost driver!

"Thank goodness you girls found me," the driver said. "First my cell phone died, and now my car won't start. I was wondering if I'd need to spend the night here."

"Don't worry, we can help you get to town," Mia said.

Just then, the friends heard buzzing overhead. It was Stephanie in her sea plane.

"Stephanie, come in, over!" Olivia said into her walkie-talkie.

"I read you loud and clear," Stephanie replied from up above. "It looks like you found our lost driver. I'll get help. Over and out!"

A short while later, a tow truck pulled up to the clearing.

"I don't know how I can thank you girls," the driver said.

Olivia smiled. "It was really Goldie who helped us rescue you. And it looks like she's already found her reward."

Goldie, who was no longer full, was eagerly munching a fresh pile of seeds.

A week later, after school, the friends came to visit Mia again at the Heartlake Vet.

"How's Goldie?" Aunt Sophie asked when they arrived.

"Just fine." Olivia smiled. "It turns out, she likes the seeds the driver brought even more than the ones in my mom's garden. So now we're all happy."

"What do you mean?" Emma asked.

"Well," Olivia said, "Goldie's happy because she has a new favorite snack. My mom's happy because her garden is growing again. And I'm happy because I'm not in trouble with my mom."

"What about your dad?" Mia asked.

Olivia laughed. "He's happy because he can finally get a good night's sleep!"

Fantastic Feathers

Emma was so inspired by Goldie on their forest adventure, that she decided to make a fun necklace out of colorful feathers! Follow her design steps to make your own original jewelry.

You'll Need

- Two feathers (of different sizes)
- String (4 in.)
- Tape
- Ribbon
- Colorful beads
- Scissors

Step 1

Start with a four-inch-long piece of string. Using the tape, attach one feather to each end of the string. Wrap the ends of the feathers with tape several times to make sure they're secure.

Step 1

Step 2a

Step 2b

Step 2

Bring both ends of the string together and attach with tape (2a). Wrap a piece of ribbon around it to hide the tape (2b). You can tie the ribbon in a bow, and decorate the ends with beads. Use a knot to hold each of the beads in place.

Ready!

Step 3

Slide a longer piece of ribbon through the loop at the top to complete the necklace. Wear this pretty, homemade jewelry with your favorite outfit, attached to your backpack, or wherever you like!

If you don't have real feathers at home, try making Emma's necklace using felt feathers instead. Draw a feather outline onto a colorful piece of felt, cut it out, and follow the steps like normal.

It's as easy as one, two, three!

19

Cozy Nest

If you had a pet bird, here's what it would need to stay happy.

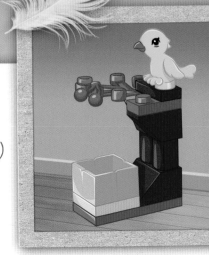

cage

toys
(like a swing)

bird house

seeds

water feeder

Do you want to try your hand at drawing Goldie? Just follow the steps to learn how! Remember to color Goldie's feathers bright yellow for a finishing touch.

Which type of bird would match your personality the best? Check out the guide below to see which bird would be the perfect feathery friend for you!

If:

You can't imagine your life without music, just like Andrea, the best bird for you would be a singing **canary**.

You love science as much as Olivia, you would like an **African gray parrot**. It's an exceptionally intelligent bird with speaking skills.

You enjoy hanging out with all your friends, like Stephanie, you would match a **zebra finch**. These birds love gathering in big groups.

You love anything bold and colorful, like Emma, you would adore an **Ara parrot**. You could look at its beautiful feathers all day!

You are fond of animals, just like Mia, **any bird** would be your perfect match! After all, what you enjoy most is taking care of animals and giving them affection.

Learn to Draw Goldie:

Bird's-Eye View

The friends are playing on the beach, and there are lots of cute critters hanging out with them! Can you spot all the crabs and turtles hidden in the photo?

Turtles 4

Crabs 5

Find out how good your memory is. Study the picture to the right for one minute, then cover it with a sheet of paper and answer the questions below.

1. Who is flying the sea plane?
a. Stephanie and Olivia
b. Only Stephanie
c. Emma and Stephanie

2. What color is the flag on the sand castle?
a. Blue
b. Pink
c. There is no flag

3. What type of shoes does Mia have on?
a. Sneakers
b. Boots
c. Flip-flops

4. What is visible in the distance?
a. A lighthouse
b. An old mill
c. City Hall

Tasty Treats

Goldie's love of seeds inspired Mia to make a special salad with sunflower seeds in it! Follow the recipe below to make your own fresh salad.

Ingredients:

- Lettuce
- 1 tomato (diced)
- Feta cheese (crumbled)
- A handful of sunflower seeds
- 2 tablespoons of olive oil
- 1 clove of garlic (minced)
- A pinch of salt and pepper

Tear a handful of washed lettuce leaves and put them in a bowl. With a parent's help, dice the tomato. Add the tomato and crumbled Feta cheese to the bowl. For dressing, mix the olive oil with the minced garlic, salt, and pepper. Pour the dressing over the salad.

Sprinkle with sunflower seeds, and enjoy!

Hide-and-Seek

After helping find the lost driver in the Whispering Woods, the friends decided to play a game of hide-and-seek in the forest. Can you figure out whose eyes are missing from the picture below?

stephanie

Friends :) | Mommy | Daddy

Andrea: Olivia, I saw your mom in the café yesterday. Her hairdo was . . . interesting.

Olivia: Ha-ha! That's because while she was fixing her hair, all the lights in the house went out.

Emma: Really? What happened?

Olivia: Well, I was testing my new invention, and something went wrong . . .

Heartlake City News

Around Town

The Pet Salon will host a pet-styling class on Tuesday. Bring your pooch for some pampering!

Heartlake High will be showcasing its annual fall chorus concert Friday night.

The Heartlake City Pool will offer free water-aerobics classes! If interested, contact Stephanie.

Fabulous Fur

*E*nrique Gonzalez, the world-famous pet stylist, will be visiting the Pet Salon on Tuesday to give pet owners his best tips. Stop by the salon at four o'clock to meet the master and learn his tricks.

READ MORE

Talk of the Day

*W*hen our lead reporter heard about Mia, Emma, Olivia, Stephanie, and Andrea's forest adventure, she had to get the scoop! The girls insisted Goldie the canary saved the day. Here's what Goldie had to say:

"Tweet, tweet!"

Splish-Splash

Weather

82° F

The Heartlake City Pool held a swimsuit fashion show by the pool this past Saturday. Many people attended, but Mayor Oliver's 1920s bathing suit stole the show! Check out the awesome pictures from the event below.

Puzzle of the Day

Look at the mystery picture to the right. Can you recognize where in Heartlake City this photo was taken?

- Pet Salon
- Café
- Swimming Pool
- Beauty Shop

ANSWER

This puzzle was sent by Olivia.

10:05

Forest Tracks

There are three different ways for the friends to find the lost driver in the Whispering Woods below. Using different colored markers, trace the path each girl should take. You can cross paths, but make sure not to use the same road twice!

29

Pool Pizzaz

Whenever they hang out at the Heartlake City Pool, the friends like to add fun accessories to their swimming outfits. Stephanie chose a sparkly bracelet, and Mia put on a Hawaiian lei. Olivia and Emma decided to wear a pretty sun hat and flower! If you could add a special accessory to your poolside outfit, what would it be?

In between splashing in the pool and relaxing in the sun, the friends came up with a trivia quiz to pass the time. The subject is birds, in honor of Goldie! Do you know the answers to all the questions below? Read the sentences and mark them "**T**" for "TRUE" or "**F**" for "FALSE."

1. There are more than 10,000 different species of birds around the world.

   T

2. Penguins live at the North Pole.

   F

3. Many birds have hollow bones, making them very light.

   T

4. Hummingbirds can fly backward.

   T

5. Because they have so many feathers, ostriches can fly very fast.

   F

6. Flamingos eat with their heads upside down!

   T

Answers

Pet Personalities   p. 2-3

Olivia

Mia

Andrea

Emma

Stephanie

Cat

Horse

Bird

Butterfly

Dog

Dream Lanterns   p. 4-5

Olivia

Stephanie   Emma   Mia   Andrea

Heartlake City News   p. 11

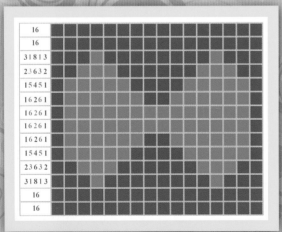

Silly Story   p. 12-13

Bird's-Eye View   p. 22-23

4
5

1-c, 2-b, 3-c, 4-a

Hide-and-Seek   p. 25
Stephanie

Puzzle of the Day   p. 27
Swimming Pool

Forest Tracks   p. 28-29

Pool Pizzaz   p. 31
T, F, T, T, F, T